MW00904757

This edition published in 1994 by
SMITHMARK Publishers Inc.,
16 East 32nd Street, New York,
NY 10016.

SMITHMARK books are available for bulk purchase for sales promotion and premium use. For details write or call the manager of special sales, SMITHMARK Publishers Inc., 16 East 32nd Street, New York,
NY 10016; (212) 532-6600.

Produced by Brompton Books Inc.
15 Sherwood Place
Greenwich, CT 06830

ISBN 0-8317-1652-5

Printed in Hong Kong

10 9 8 7 6 5 4 3 2 1

"'VAN GOOL'S'"

Hansel and Gretel

A poor woodcutter and his wife lived in a small cottage with their two children, a boy named Hansel, and his sister, Gretel. One night, the children overheard their parents talking in the kitchen. There was a great famine in the land. The family had little food left and no money. "We must take the children, and go deep into the woods to search for food," said the father in a worried tone, "or else we will all starve."

Gretel was alarmed, as they had never ventured deep into the woods before. "Don't worry," said Hansel. "I'll drop some pebbles along the path so we can find our way home." The next morning, as they set off, Hansel began to lay the trail.

That evening, the woodcutter built a fire and said, "Wait here, children. We will go further into the woods and see if we can find anything to eat." Their parents set off with heavy hearts.

Hansel and Gretel watched them disappear among the trees. Then they lay down beside the fire and fell asleep.

When the fire was only a pile of ashes, the children woke up cold and hungry. Their parents had been gone a long time.

"What shall we do, Hansel?" sobbed Gretel. "Wait until the moon comes out," he said cheerfully, "and by its light, we will follow the pebbles back home."

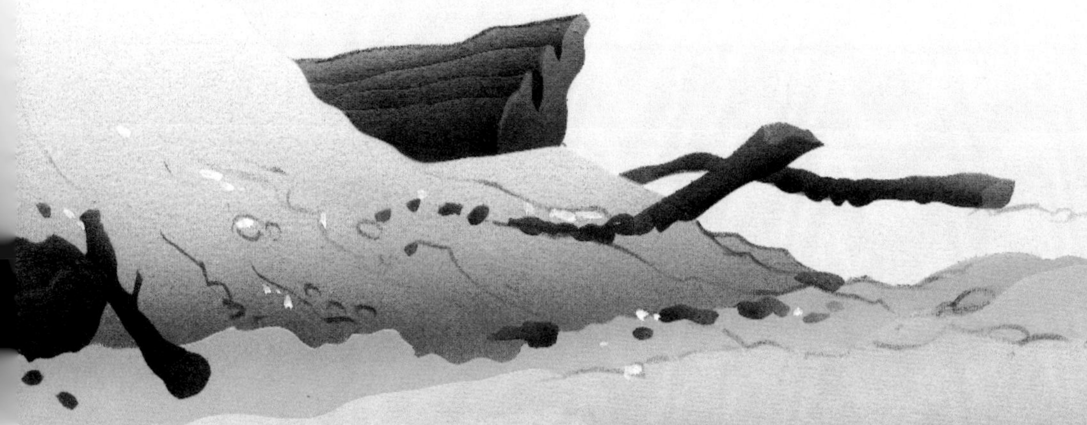

When the moon rose in the sky, they made their way back to the path. In the bright light, they soon found the pebbles.

"Look, here's one," cried Gretel. "And another!" They began their journey home.

By dawn, they were back at the clearing where their cottage stood. They ran into the house, calling, "Father, Mother, we're home!"

Their father was so glad to see them. In the dark, he had missed the path back to the children and was setting out to search for them. Happy to be together again, they forgot about their problems. . . for a short while.

But soon after, the crops failed again and the woodcutter told his wife, “We must return to the forest, and look for food.” When Gretel heard this she told Hansel to go out and collect some pebbles, just in case they got lost again.
But it was late at night, and the door to the cottage was locked!

In the morning, their mother gave them each a piece of bread, the last in the house. "Eat yours," Hansel whispered to Gretel, "and I will drop the crumbs from mine on the path." Trailing behind the others, Hansel threw down his crumbs to mark their way.

But he forgot about the birds, who were also hungry. They swooped down to the path and ate up all his crumbs.

While Hansel and Gretel were playing in the woods, they lost sight of their parents. Unconcerned, they tried to retrace their steps, but couldn't find a single crumb to guide them.

"Never mind, Hansel," said Gretel bravely, "we shall just have to find our own way home."

The children walked for a long time. They were tired and hungry when, suddenly, a magnificent white peacock appeared before them.

"Follow me," she screeched.

The bird led Hansel and Gretel to a clearing in the forest, where they found a wonderful little house made of sweets and cake! "Oh!" they cried, unable to believe their eyes.

At once, the children began to pull off pieces of the shutters and to pick the lollipop flowers. They were alarmed when they heard a shrill voice call from inside:

Nibble, nibble, like a mouse,
Who is nibbling at my house?

"It's only the wind," answered Hansel and Gretel nervously, eating as fast as they could.

But they stopped in fright when an ugly old woman came out and beckoned to them. They were about to run away when she said sweetly, "Why don't you come in for a while?" Unwisely, Hansel and Gretel followed her into the house.

Although she pretended to be kind, the old woman was really a wicked witch, who liked to eat little children. But she put Hansel and Gretel at ease by offering them a splendid feast.

The witch set the table with more food than the children had ever seen. There were pastries and cakes, chocolates and sweets, delicious drinks – everything you could imagine. Hansel and Gretel spent all afternoon eating until they were so full they could eat no more.

The witch sent them to bed, and returned to the kitchen to plot and scheme.

"They are thin," she said to herself. "But if I feed the boy large meals, he will soon be fat enough to eat. And then I'll deal with his sister."

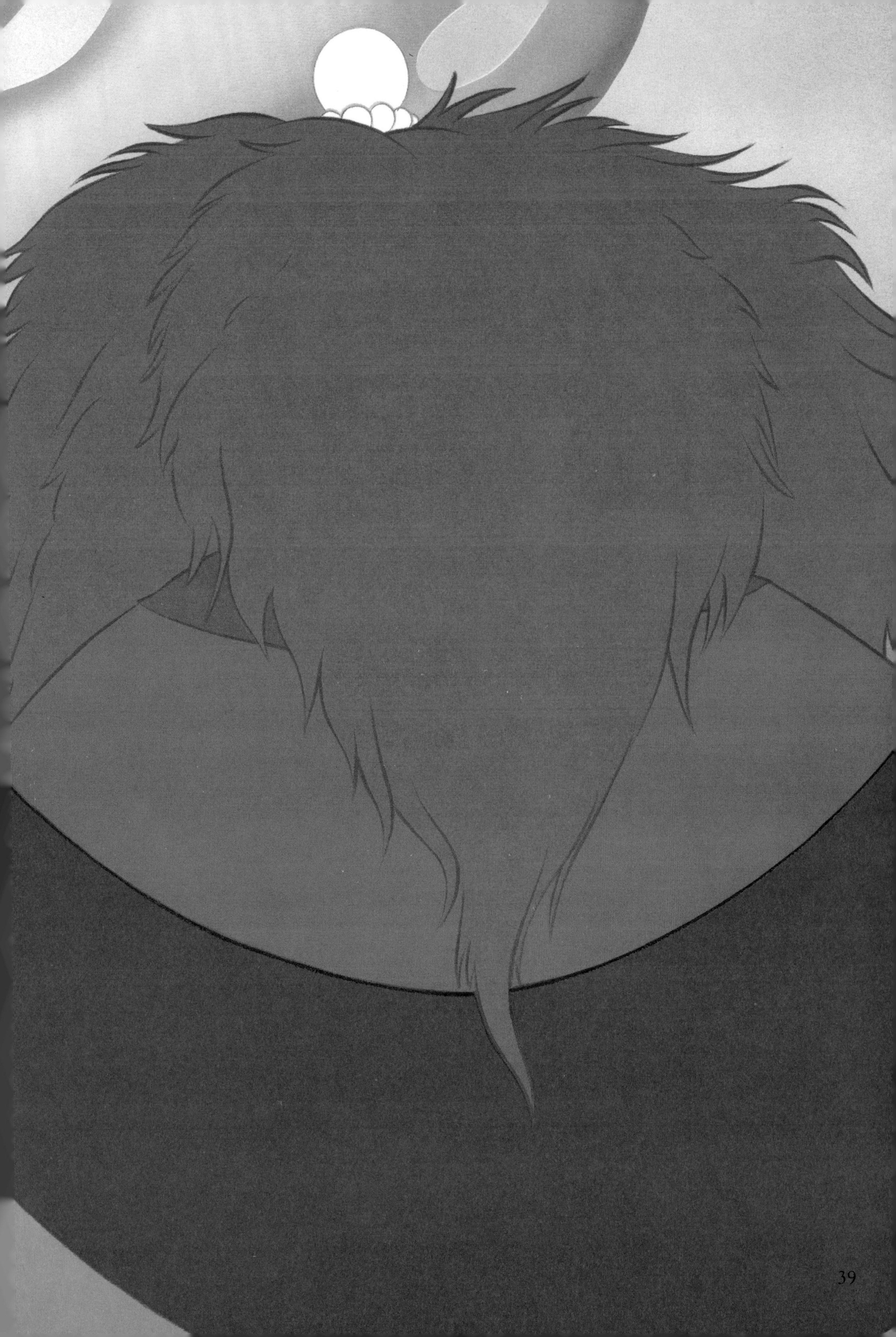

The next morning, the cruel witch pulled Hansel from his bed and locked him in a cage in the cellar. "And there you'll stay," she cackled, "until you're fat enough to eat. Meanwhile, your sister can do all the housework!"

"Let me go!" cried the frightened boy. But the witch paid no attention to his cries.

The witch woke Gretel, saying, "Fetch water from the stream and clean the house! You are also to cook a large meal every day for your brother, until he is fat enough for me to eat!" Gretel was terrified, but she had no choice. So she started her chores.

Gretel worked hard, but the cruel witch gave her only scraps to eat. These she shared with the mice who came to the table. All the time she thought only of how she could free Hansel so they could both escape.

Every day, the witch visited Hansel. "Stick your finger through the bars so I can tell how fat you're getting," she said. (She was so short-sighted she could hardly see.) But Hansel was clever, and stuck a chicken bone through the bars. The witch pinched it, thinking it was his finger, and couldn't understand why he wasn't growing fatter.

After several weeks, the witch lost patience. "Fat or thin, I will eat him today!" she declared. She handed Gretel a bundle of sticks and told her to build a fire in the oven. Gretel knew this was her only chance!

When the fire was blazing, she asked the witch, "How can I tell if the oven is hot enough?"

"Like this, you foolish girl," snapped the witch, and she bent over the oven to feel the heat. In an instant, Gretel had pushed the witch into the oven and slammed the door tightly shut!

"Hansel! We're free!" she cried happily, running to unlock the cage. "The witch is dead!" The children hugged each other tightly and danced around the room.

Then they went and searched the cottage, looking for the witch's hidden treasures – sparkling jewels she had stolen from other people who had also lost their way in the woods. They filled two sacks with precious stones. They had found a fortune!

"Now, let's get away from here!" cried Hansel. And they ran out into the forest searching for a way home. Finally, they found a stream they knew. But it was too wide to wade or swim across.

Gretel spotted a beautiful white swan out on the water. She called:

Swan, swan, here we stand,
Hansel and Gretel, on the land,
Stepping stones and bridge we lack,
Please carry us over on your white back.

The swan kindly came to the bank of the stream and, in turn, took them across the water. They were now close to home.

Their father had just come out of the cottage to chop wood when Hansel and Gretel ran into his arms. He was overjoyed to see them alive and well. He had searched the whole countryside for news of them.

"Come and see what we've brought home!" cried Hansel excitedly.

The children tipped the sacks of precious stones onto the table, and their father picked one up in wonder.

"We'll never be poor or go hungry again!" said Hansel. "Mother, come quickly!" Their mother came to join them and they all danced for joy!